From
Buddy Blair

Being brave for

~~Bailey /~~

Being Brave for Bailey

Corey Gut, DVM

Illustrated by Jaime Myers

Second Edition

Published by Corey Gut, DVM

Text and Illustrations Copyright © 2014 Corey Gut, DVM

For information or ordering copies, visit our website at www.BeingBraveforBailey.com

Contact us at BBFB333@gmail.com

ISBN: 978-0-578-14849-6

Library of Congress Control Number: 2014915123

Printed in the USA

Signature Book Printing, www.sbpbooks.com

This book is dedicated to

every child who has loved a pet

with their whole heart and

has had to say

goodbye.

I have a friend,

so loving and sweet.

We've grown up together.

He sleeps at my feet.

He's my very best friend.

I've loved him for years.

He makes me laugh

and calms all my fears.

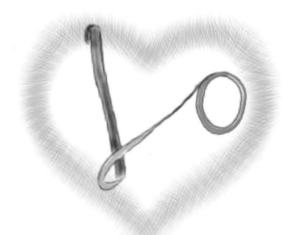

Over the years we've had

good times and great fun.

But lately, it seems,

the laughs are all gone.

Bailey now moves slowly

and his tail rarely wags.

It seems my dog's sad

and his head often sags.

Bailey is sick

and he hurts every day.

He won't eat his food

and refuses to play.

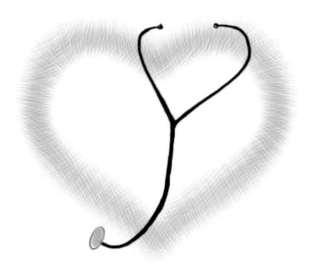

Our vet says it's time,
he really should rest.

Now we need to do
for him what is best.

But saying goodbye

just seems so unfair.

This burden is simply

too heavy to bear.

Because I love Bailey,

I need to be strong.

So he doesn't suffer,

we can't wait too long.

It's okay to cry.

My heart hurts so bad.

I kiss him and remember

the good times we've had.

The time has now come.

We are off to the vet.

I still remember

the first time we met.

He's been my friend
through good times and bad.
It's being so close
that makes this so sad.

"I love you"

The vet greets us warmly,

her words kind and sweet.

I whisper "I love you"

as he looks up from my feet.

I squeeze his warm body

and hug him and cry,

As he is sent to a safe place,

I tell him "goodbye."

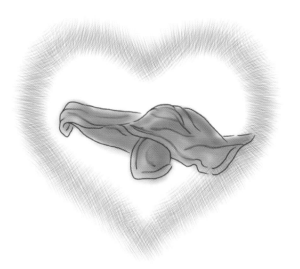

He peacefully passes

and takes one last breath.

I'm strong and I'm brave

as I face Bailey's death.

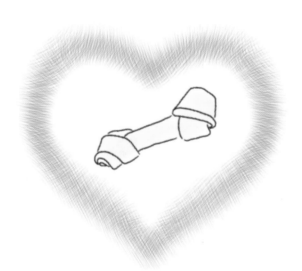

He'll always be with me,

though our bodies now part.

I know he's still close

and lives on in my heart.

I'll hold on to our memories,

his smell and warm touch.

And hope to meet another,

to love just as much.

'Tis better to have loved and lost

Than never to have loved at all

　　　　　- Alfred Lord Tennyson

Bailey

In Memory

Activity ideas for further support

Make a scrapbook, a photo album or a memory box

Plant a tree or a flower bed in your yard in honor of your pet

Find a star in the sky and name it after your pet

Make a clay paw print or clip some fur and tie it with pretty ribbon

Make a holiday ornament with your pet's photo

Write a poem, short story or a song about your pet

Create a website or social media page to honor your pet

Draw or paint a picture of your pet

Record stories and favorite memories about your pet in a journal

Make a bracelet or necklace with letter beads spelling your pet's name

About the Author

Corey is a veterinarian in Bloomfield Hills, Michigan. Her previous veterinary roles have included international surgeon, wildlife doctor, Earthwatch marine mammal rescue and rehabilitator, veterinary counselor and professor. Although she has loved working in a wide variety of veterinary fields, she finds her current job of caring for pets and their families the most personally rewarding.

After 10 years in practice, Corey wrote this book to provide parents with a tool to broach the difficult subject of euthanasia and pet loss with their children.